This is my little brother Leroy.

1

When Granny sees Leroy she says, "What a sweet little boy!"

When Grandpa sees Leroy he says,
"What a bundle of joy!"

But Granny and Grandpa don't know the real Leroy.

The real Leroy is an annoying little boy.

Leroy annoys Mum. He jumps on the table.

He puts coins down the toilet.

And he has a very loud voice.

Sweets!
Sweets!
Sweets!

SWEETS

Leroy annoys my big sister.

He fiddles with her little bottles.

Leroy annoys the cat.

She thinks he is too noisy.

Cuddle!
Cuddle!
Cuddle!

And Leroy annoys me!

He scribbles on
my books.

He muddles up my toys

and pops my bubbles.

He spoils all my games.

Yes, Leroy is a destroyer!

But sometimes, just sometimes, I enjoy having a little brother.

I like to tumble about with him.

He gives me nice cuddles.

And there is one time when
Leroy isn't annoying at all.

When he's asleep!